THE MEDITERRANEAN
AND THE MEDITERRANEAN WORLD
IN THE AGE OF PHILIP II